*

More Prefabulous Animiles

*

MORE PREFABULOUS ANIMILES

by
James Reeves
and
Edward Ardizzone

HEINEMANN

William Heinemann Ltd

15 Queen Street, Mayfair, London W1X 8BE

LONDON MELBOURNE TORONTO
JOHANNESBURG AUCKLAND

*

First published in 1975
Text © James Reeves 1975
Illustrations © Edward Ardizzone 1975
434 95894 8

Printed and bound in Great Britain by
Cox & Wyman Ltd, London,
Fakenham and Reading

TO
PHILIP
AND GELDA ARDIZZONE

*

CONTENTS

LET NO ONE

Let no one suppose
That the creatures he knows—
The sheep and the cow,
The swag-bellied sow,
The hamster, the hare,
The badger, the bear,
The pigeon, the widgeon,
The bats in the air,
The deer in the park,
The jubilant lark,
The camel, the dingo,
The flaming flamingo—
Let no one suppose
That creatures like those
Are all that the animal kingdom contains.
If that's what you think
Then go to a shrink,
A qualified doctor who knows about brains.

When night is approaching
And poachers are poaching,
There are creatures that lurk,
They linger and lurk
When you're trying to work.
You're as pale as your book
And you hardly dare look.
There's a SOMETHING there
At the head of the stair.

2

Its breathing is slow and its odour is musky,
And its paws you are sure must be horny and husky
And everywhere's dusky
And you think if you turn on the light,
It might bite, it might smite,
It might cackle or whimper
Or whinney or simper
Or laugh.
If anyone thinks that the gracious giraffe
Is the tallest,
The microbe the smallest,
The serpent the longest,
The lion the strongest,
The cheetah the quickest,
If anyone thinks that the donkey's the thickest
Of creatures on earth, he had best think again,
For animal annals are known to contain
The records of creatures quite different from these,
Faster and vaster,
Milder and wilder,
Louder and longer
And thicker and stronger
Than any you've seen on the box or in books.
So if any suppose that the creatures he knows
Are all that the animal world can discover,
Let him turn this page over
And there he will see what the experts agree,
When they leaf through their notebooks and
    thumb through their files,
Are breath-stopping, eye-popping ANIMILES,
Your actual PREFABULOUS ANIMILES!

3

THE OZALID

The Ozalid is not a thing
   I greatly care to meet.
Its neck is like a piece of string;
   Its ears are on its feet.

Its single eye is on a swivel;
   This way and that it spins.
Its smudgy nose is apt to snivvle;
   It has three flipperfins.

It has three flipperfins, my friend;
   Its tail is three feet long,
And at its hard and horny end
   It has a fatal prong—

A fatal but a useful prong,
  With which it spikes its prey,
The agile tape-fish lean and long,
  The chipworm sad and grey.

But once (I tremblingly relate)
  An Ozalid had the luck—
The evil luck, the groojus fate—
  To spear a sleeping duck.

Enraged, the duck took instant wing.
  Its flight was straight and strong.
The Ozalid, that hapless thing,
  Could not withdraw its prong.

Hung by its tail beneath the bird,
  The Ozalid soared aloft.
Cries of amazement soon were heard
  From Hull to Lowestoft.

When folks at Folkestone saw the sight
  They clamoured 'How absurd
To see an Ozalid in flight
  Transported by a bird!'

THE TROKE

I celebrate the various Troke.
   'Why "various"?' I hear you cry.
Be patient, dears, and hold your smoke*,
   For I to you will make reply,
Giving you reasons multifarious
Why this strange beast is known as various.

* 'hold your smoke' means much the same as 'hold your
fire, wait'. There is no fire without smoke, so why not 'Hold
your smoke'?

His hide is various, for a start,
  Being yellowish with purple bars
And spots and dots of divers hue
  And other sorts of stripes and stars.
Towards the coming on of night
He is a rather daunting sight.

But that's not all. He has four legs,
  One long, three short—or *vice versa*.
He moves in circles, more or less
  Now right, now left; and, what is worser,
His feet are ill-assorted too—
One rough, three smooth, two pink, two blue.

Sometimes he huffs, as if in anger,
  Sometimes he shlurps in amorous vein.
When hungry, he's inclined to whindle;
  The moon evokes a different strain:
Then hear the high nocturnal tone
That freezes all your flesh to stone.

In mood and temper too, I hear,
  None is more various than the Troke.
At times he sulks in gloomiest dudgeon,
  At times enjoys a simple joke.
But if you laugh at him, my dears,
He'll *snip* you like a pair of shears.

His diet too is heterogeneous
  (Or 'mixed', to use a simpler word)—
One day he wants no food but nuts,
  Next day it's mice; but on the third
A rival Troke he's apt to slaughter,
Or else he'll fast and live on water.

He is not loved, I must confess,
  Among the Animile community.
He is too unpredictable,
  His life has neither use nor unity.
I tolerate, but would not stroke,
The broody, moody, various Troke.

THE DIZZ

Oh, have you seen the beauteous Dizz
And heard his soft 'Biz-biz! biz-biz!'
As through the sumptious evening hour
He oscillates from flower to flower.
His long discerning nose can tell
The difference of smell from smell,
As on his busy way he goes
From honeybunch to sugarose.

He has six wings, not all the same,
Two mauve, two emerald, two flame,
On which he trundles here and there
All in the sumptious summer air,
Or with his plushy wings spread wide
He does the gorgeous glitterglide,
Something between a dive and dance,
Which puts the watchers in a trance.
'It is,' they sigh, 'it is, it is
The ultraspecial, long-nosed Dizz.

The Queen Dizz has no wings at all,
But sits at home in Honey Hall
Enjoying the galooshus things
Her ever-helpful helpmeet brings.
How fortunate if *you* should spy
So rare a creature in the sky
And hear the soft 'Biz-biz! biz-biz!'
Emitted by the beauteous Dizz.
Oh, how his six wings whirr and whizz!

THE KWACKAGEE

Back in the bleak and blurry days
When all was murk and mystery—
That is (if I may mint a phrase)
Before the dawn of history.
Professors think there used to be,
Not far from Waikee-waike,
A monster called the Kwackagee,
A sort of flying snake.

This animile, they all agree,
Was forty feet in length,
Would spiral up the tallest tree
And then with all his strength
Propel himself with sinuous grace
And undulation muscular
To find another feeding-place
In some far vale crepuscular.

Expert opinions are two
About his mode of travel;
Professor Grommit holds one view;
The other, Doctor Gravvle.
Grommit believes he could give off
Some kind of speed-emulsion;
The Doctor, ever prone to scoff,
Postulates jet-propulsion.

In prehistoric Waikee-waike,
The men (if men there were),
Would they in breathless terror quake
To hear that rattling whirr
As flew the monster through the sky?
Or would they brave the foe
With missile and with battle-cry?—
The experts do not know.

THE NOG

The fragrant vale of Chatnagog
Harbours the small and sprightly Nog.
His shape is oval, like an egg;
He has one short and springy leg,
On which, though he himself is small—
No bigger than a croquet ball—
He bounces a prodigious way
Here, there and everywhere all day,
Six, seven or eight feet at a bound,
Sometimes in mid-air twirling round
Or somersaulting high as high
All in the blue and boiling sky.

The Nog is an endearing fellow.
His shining skin is lemon yellow.
His mate is of a duller hue,
But she, like him, can trill and coo;
Like him she chirrups as she bounces,
But if some direful danger pounces
The dog-toothed hawk of Chatnagog
Or, even worse, the hawk-toothed dog,

A sharp, shrill twitter of alarm
Gives notice of impending harm.
That instant she will lie as still
As stones upon a desert hill,
Whose colour she will imitate,
Huddled beside her trusty mate.
But when no peril hovers near,
From lurking foe the coast is clear,

In short, when all is safe once more,
Why then the cry is 'Vive le sport!'
(I quote in French the exclamation
In tribute to this sporting nation.)
Then down the fragrant valley see
Both Nog and Noglets bouncing free,
Grown-ups and children, old and young.
Now let him spring who never sprung!

(Well yes, I know—it should be 'sprang' . . .)
You never saw so spry a gang
As gather for the bouncing races
From near and far and other places;
And many a sporting writer names
The Chatnagog Olympic games
As much the jolliest of the season.
I must admit they have good reason.

But not without a sense of shame
I must describe a different game.
Some boy Nogs, bigger than the rest—
'Them Noggoes' they are called in jest—
These boy Nogs of the ruder sort
Without a proper sense of sport
Engage in what they call 'Nog bowls',
In which by turns each player rolls
A Noglet to a central spot
Where sits an old Nog called 'the pot'.
With raucous glee the Noggoes roll
The Noglets to the 'pot' or goal.
This game the Noglets do not like
And are prepared to go on strike.
In time the older Nogs, no doubt,
Will stamp the cruel practice out,
That such things shall no more disgrace
This cheerful, harmless, sprightly race,
And innocent mirth alone resound
In Chatnagog's delightful ground.

THE HOVERWING

Italians think there's nothing sweeter
Than what they call the *dolce vita*,
While other folk—and they are plenty—
Extol the *Dolce far niente*.
The Boo-boos of the Blissful Ocean
Express a similar emotion
When, basking by their sandy caves,
They contemplate the wimbling waves.
From care and pain their lives are free;
They fish for fish upon the sea;
When skies are clear and winds are calm,
They climb the graceful pogo palm

In quest of its galooshus fruit
With which they eat the gah-gah root.
But, as I said, their dearest wish
Is on the sea to fish for fish—
The salamo, the polypod,
The megaprawn, the blue-nosed cod
And other denizens of savour,
Some for their texture, some their flavour.

Ah me! there is no way of life
Without its special source of strife,
Without the occasional disappointment.
Such is the blow-fly in the ointment;
Such is the maggot in the peach,
The broken bottle on the beach.
What garden is without a weed?

—Enough of this. Let me proceed:
Even the Boo-boos have a woe;
It is that dire-destructive foe;
It is that most horrendous thing,
The greater saw-backed Hoverwing.
A larger version of the whale,
It has a forked and furious tail;
Its sickening, oleaginous stench

Can make the sturdiest seaman blench;
Its hide repels the sharpest spear;
Its bellow fills the best with fear;
Its roar is like a hurricane.
Its forty spouts can drown in rain
The biggest craft constructed yet
And smaller vessels overset,
So cataclysmic the commotion

Occasioned on the Blissful Ocean
By that most ultra-groojus thing,
The greater saw-backed Hoverwing.
See how it somersaults and spins,
Gyrating on its turbo-fins.
See how it wallows, skims and flies,
Descending from pacific skies
To swamp their boats and terrorize
With hoarse and blood-congealing cries
The harmless Boo-boos, whose sole wish
Is but to bask and fish for fish.

You in your safe retreat may smile
To read about this animile,
But spare a thought, I do implore,
For those who, by the Blissful shore,
Pursue their harmless avocation,
The childlike, simple Boo-boo nation.

THE BOGUS-BOO

The Bogus-boo
Is a creature who
Comes out at night—and why?
He likes the air;
He likes to scare
The nervous passer-by.

Out from the park
At dead of dark
He comes with huffling pad.
If, when alone,
You hear his moan,
'Tis like to drive you mad.

He has two wings,
Pathetic things,
With which he cannot fly.
His tusks look fierce,
Yet could not pierce
The merest butterfly.

He has six ears,
But what he hears
Is very faint and small;
And with the claws
On his eight paws
He cannot scratch at all.

He looks so wise
With his owl-eyes,
His aspect grim and ghoulish;
But truth to tell,
He sees not well
And is distinctly foolish.

This Bogus-boo,
What can he do
But huffle in the dark?
So don't take fright;
He has no bite
And very little bark.

THE SNIGGLE

The Sniggle (often called the Snyle)
Is not a lovely animile.
He has four legs equipped with claws,
Another six with sucker-paws.
When thus he climbs up walls of rock,
You hear his suckers go *plick-plock*.
Plick-plock plick-plock—by night he crawls
On gutter-pipes and roofs and walls.
The Sniggle's is a groujus noise,
Dreaded by all offending boys.

39

The Sniggle lurks in Woeful Woods
And noses out his favourite foods—
The slow-worm and the blunderbug,
The slurp, the giant hairy slug,
Also that most galooshus dish,
The frozocrumm or finger-fish.

The full-grown adult Snyle (or Sniggle)
Has one long horn which he can wiggle,
Emitting a ferocious bray
With which to terrorize his prey.
When terrorized himself, the Snyle
Secretes a black and fexious bile.
The men who flourished long ago

Beside the River Gallimo
Use it to smear upon their skins
To scare away the gobbolins.
Others, for more artistic ends,
Employed it to surprise their friends
By making abstract wall designs
In flowing and expressive lines.

Noxious as is the Sniggle male,
To see his mate your heart would fail,
For she is squalid, squat and small.
She has no bile, no claws at all;
Her horn is short and will not wiggle,
Her only note a nervous giggle.
She lives on scraps her mate supplies.
I say in short, and none denies,
The female Sniggle is a creature
Without a sole redeeming feature.
So I conclude with jubilation
This sad, this groojus recitation.

Far in the land of Waikee-waike
Among the trees by Happi Lake
There lives a curious Animile—
To wit, the fragrant Pickadile.
The denizens of Waikee-waike
Pursue him for his perfume's sake.
This perfume is a cross between
Lemon verbena and quinine.
Bees, butterflies, small birds as well
Are drawn towards the sumptious smell.
This satisfies the creature's pride
For he is somewhat dandified.
This superelegant Animile
Is fashioned in rococo style.

His smile is devious and dental;
His limbs are lithe and ornamental;
On two he walks, or rather glides,
And two hang drooping at his sides,
Except when he is culling flowers,
Which, when he's hungry, he devours.
His scaly tail is long and strong;
With it, when roused, *'bing-bong! bing-bong!'*

A battery of telling blows
He rains upon all jealous foes.
But, truth to tell, he has not many.
A pair of sinuous antennae
Protrude from out his fulgious curls,
And these he preens, he pranks, he twirls.
With a tall tuft his top is decked,
Plumy, curvaceous and erect.

If you should go to Waikee-waike
And stroll beside the Happi Lake,
Observe this fragrant Animile,
The condescending Pickadile

As joysomely he trots and trips,
A sprightly *chanson* on his lips—
That is to say, upon his beak;
His voice is but a groojus squeak.

Now lesser creatures jeer at him;
They find his manner proud and prim;
They imitate his sinuous grace
And make rude noises to his face.
But all their efforts fail to rile
The odoriferous Pickadile.
Long may he glide by Happi Lake
In the far land of Waikee-waike.

THE OXYPHANTASORIUS

From times prefabulous and now long gone
The Oxyphantasorius lingers on
In deserts far from human habitation.
He is the hugest creature in creation.
His blood-congealing, grim, and bulbous figure
Is something like an elephant's, but bigger;

In shape and size the Oxyphantasorius
Has been described as *almost henrymoorius.*
Compared with him, the whale is but a sprat,
The crocodile a frog, the crow a gnat;
Compared with him, etcetera, etcetera . . .
(Make up the rest yourself, and do it betterer.)
He has a trunk, two deadly tusks, three humps,
A muscular, broad tail with which he jumps
After the manner of a kangaroo.
They tried to trap him for a private zoo,
But had to give it up; he jumped too high.
His roar would make a sergeant-major cry.
There are no ears for those Wagnerian tones,
The blaring of a thousand saxophones.
Even the master-minds at Tunbridge Wells
Could not compute those murderous decibels.

All is a wilderness where he inhabits;
All creatures cower and flee like hunted rabbits.
So how he lives remains a mystery.
Some say he feeds upon the yumyum tree;
Some say he jumps upon the native villages
Beyond the desert, which the monster pillages
And, putting the inhabitants to flight,
He gluts his juggernautical appetite.
At all events, the oxyphantasorius
Is judged by naturalists to be uxorious;
In other words the creature wants to find
A spouse with whom to propagate his kind:
It is not hunger makes him so uproarious—
He needs a female Oxyphantasorius.
This, say the experts, is what drives him on,
This late survivor from times dead and gone.

Oh what a fate were ours should he succeed
And overrun the planet with his breed!
Perish the thought; perish this nightmare too,
This oxyphantile crypto-kangaroo.
So let your prayers be lengthy and laborious
To exorcise the Oxyphantasorius.
God Save Her Majesty! Send her victorious
Against her foe, the Oxyphantasorius.